ROMAN NUMERALS I to MM

NUMERABILIA ROMANA UNO AD DUO MILA

MCMXCVI

LIBER DE DIFFICILLIMO COMPUTANDO NUMERUM

Arthur Geisert

SCHOLASTIC INC.

New York Toronto London Auckland Sydney
Mexico City New Delhi Hong Kong Buenos Aires

For art teachers
Gerald Brommer, *age* LXIX
and
Reinhold Marxhausen, *age* LXXIV

Copyright © 1996 by Arthur Geisert.
All rights reserved. Published by Scholastic Inc., 557 Broadway, New York, NY 10012, by arrangement with Houghton Mifflin Company.
Printed in the U.S.A.

ISBN 0-439-86314-7

1 2 3 4 5 6 7 8 9 10   40   14 13 12 11 10 09 08 07 06

NUMERABILIA ROMANA UNO AD DUO MILA

LIBER DE DIFFICILLIMO COMPUTANDO NUMERUM

Seven letters stand for numbers called Roman numerals. Used alone or in various combinations, they will make every number. The letters are: I, V, X, L, C, D, and M.

Count the number of pigs to find the value of each numeral.

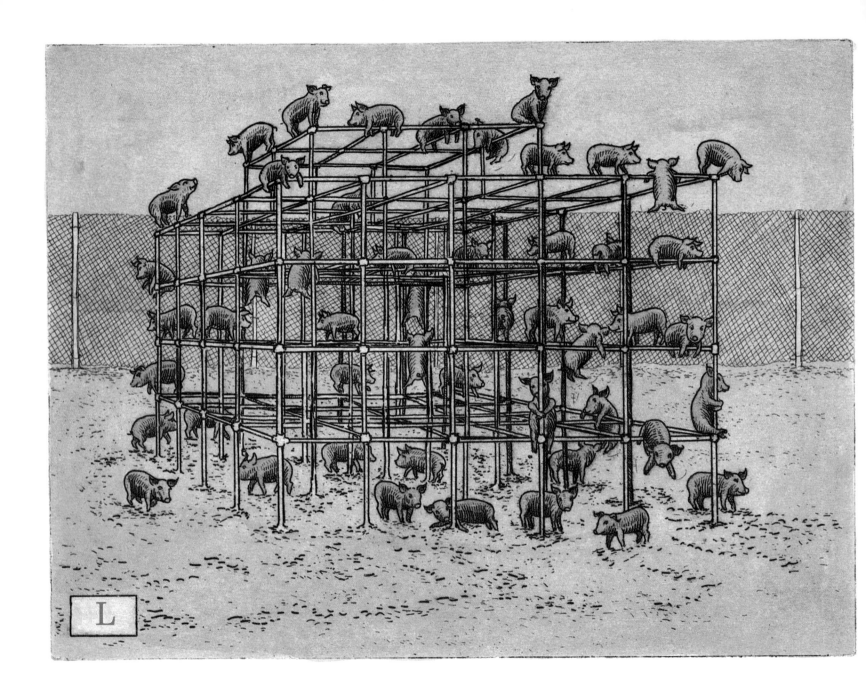

L

vi

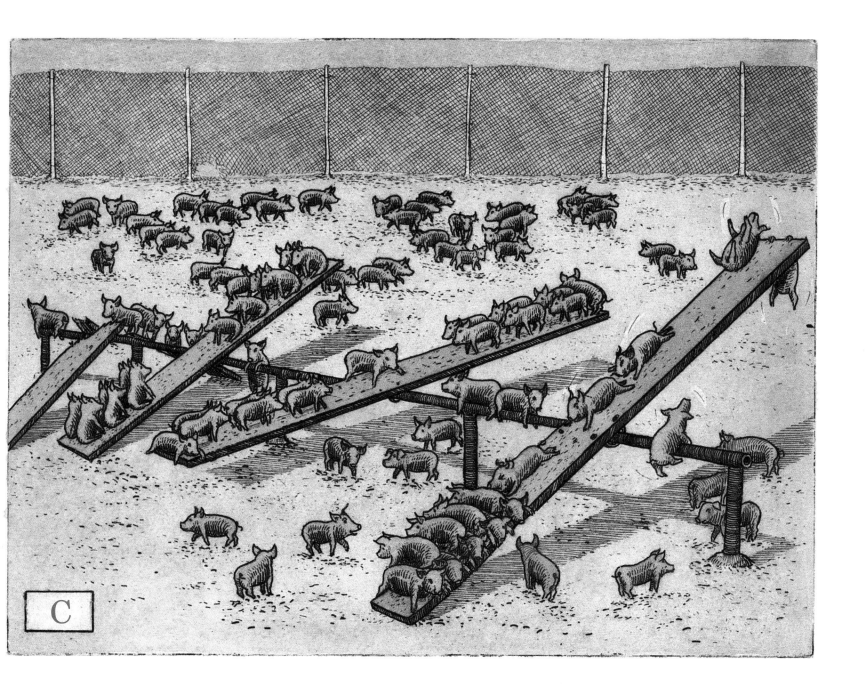

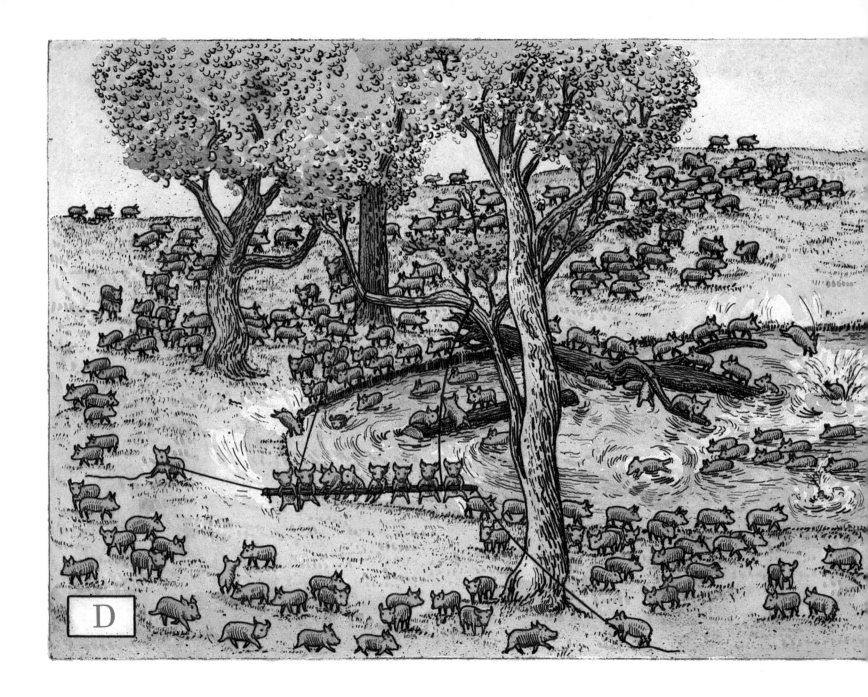

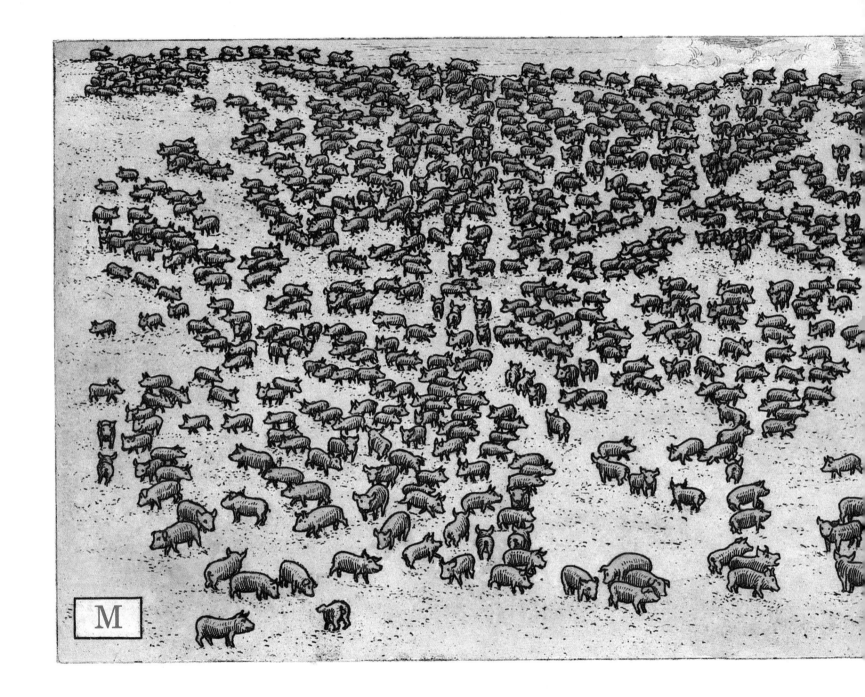

X

Roman numerals are written and read from left to right. If numerals of equal value are placed side by side, they are added.
I, X, and C may be used two and three times in a row.

V, L, and D are not used in a row because, when added, they total an existing numeral. VV=X, so X is used instead. Likewise, LL=C and DD=M.

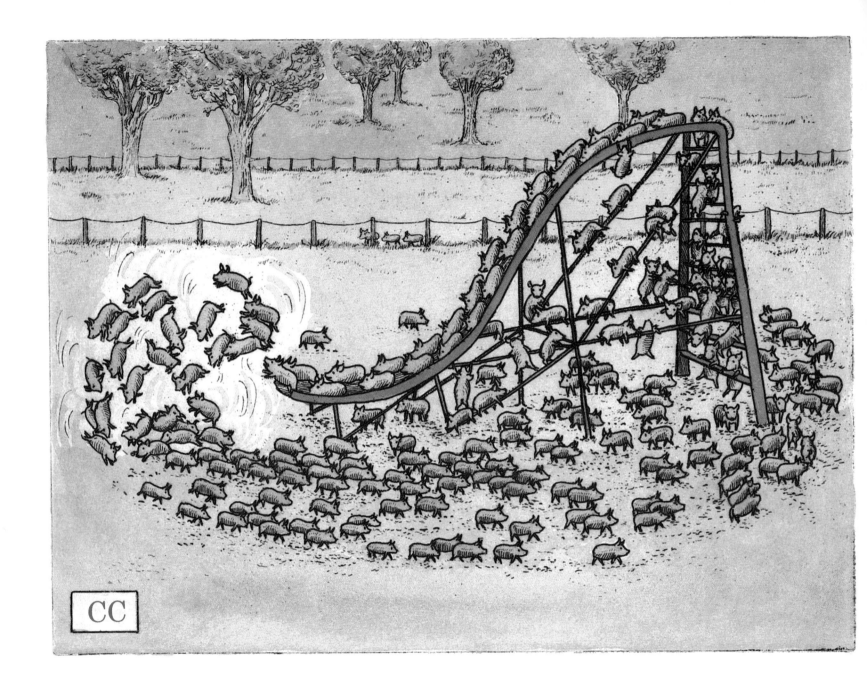

MM

M is the largest Roman numeral. It may also be used two and three times in a row, as may I, X, and C. However, unlike I, X, and C, M may be repeated many times.

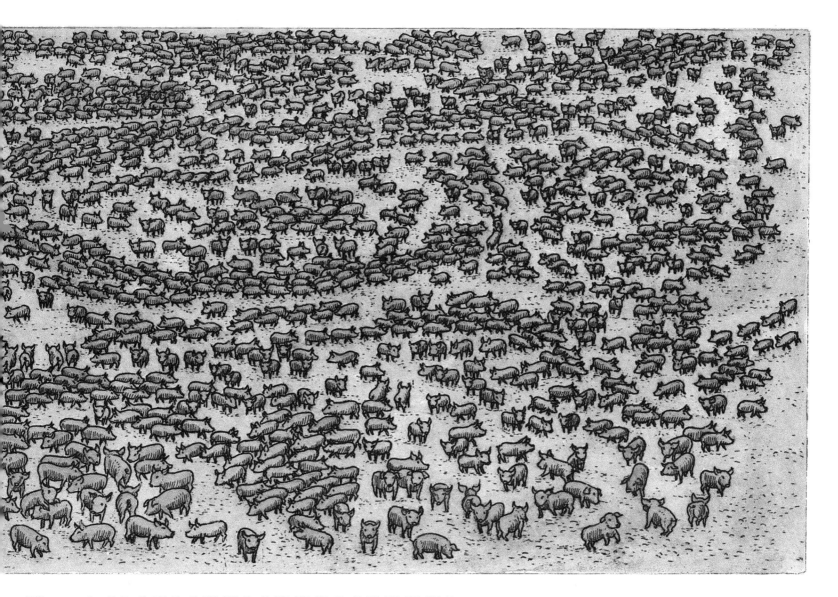

There is M, MM, MMM, MMMM, MMMMM, etcetera.

Numbers are made by adding and subtracting. When writing a Roman numeral, the largest numeral is written first, followed by numerals of equal or lesser value.

These numerals are added. However, when a smaller numeral appears before a larger numeral, it is subtracted from that numeral. IV and IX are examples.

Numerals that involve subtraction always have a four or nine in that number. XIV and XIX are examples.

In a long number, subtraction may take place more than once.
This often happens in dates. MCMXC, nineteen ninety, is an example.

The best way to learn Roman numerals is to use them.
If you don't know what the numerals listed are,
count the objects in the picture to find out.

X	Pig Houses	V	Cows
III	Tractors	XI	Evergreen trees
IV	Water tanks	IX	Storage bins

II Tire swings   VII Clouds

I Eighteen Twelve   IV Birds

X Sandbags   IV Hands

I	Nineteen Twenty-two	II	Eagles
IX	Flowerpots	I	Sixteen Twenty
XVI	Gopher holes	XX	Chain links

I	Eighteen Sixty-one	III	Trash cans
I	Nineteen Five	VL	Pigs
IV	Stone posts	I	Seventeen Fifty

XVIII Bottles
    I Seventeen Sixty-six
  IV Brown jugs

   I Eighteen Ninety
 LIV Boiler bolts
XIII Bricks

V	Saw blades	XXXVI	Pigs
I	Nineteen Hundred	I	Nineteen Forty-one
III	Urns	VI	Birds

This Book Contains

XII	Stumps	V	Barrels
XXXII	Pages	II	Mice
VII	Tire swings	IX	Cannonballs
III	Weathervanes	V	Pig statues
XXVI	Birds	II	Sundials
I	Bell	VII	Cows

MMMMDCCCLXIV Pigs